ZOO STORY

**PAIGNTON ZOO AND THE WHITLEY WILDLIFE
CONSERVATION TRUST**

Philip Knowling

HALSGROVE

First published in Great Britain in 2005

British Library Cataloguing-in-Publication Data
A CIP record for this title is available from the British Library

ISBN 1 84114 461 4

HALSGROVE
Halsgrove House
Lower Moor Way
Tiverton, Devon EX16 6SS
Tel: 01884 243242
Fax: 01884 243325
email: sales@halsgrove.com
website: www.halsgrove.com

Printed and bound by D'Auria Industrie Grafiche Spa, Italy

CONTENTS

FOREWORD

The Whitley Wildlife Conservation Trust and its associated organisations – Paignton Zoo, Living Coasts and Newquay Zoo – together comprise one of the largest conservation and education charities in the South West of England. As well as the zoos the Trust owns the largest freshwater lake in the South West, Slapton Ley, and two smaller urban nature reserves in Paignton. The Trust and the zoos also support field conservation efforts elsewhere in the United Kingdom and in Africa.

The relentless pace of urbanisation, pollution and habitat destruction so prevalent in Britain during the twentieth century seems to have slowed and people have an understanding and appreciation of the value of the natural world. Seeing animals and plants at close quarters has always been a fundamental human pleasure and one of the roles of our zoos has been to get animals and people together in safety. We hope that by inspiring visitors with the wonder and beauty of nature they will go on to do their part to protect it.

Trying to give a sense of the whole organisation to those visiting its individual parts is not easy. When the opportunity came to work with ITV Westcountry to produce a television series trying to do just that we were delighted. We wanted the series to focus on the animals, the plants and the mission rather than on the people carrying it out – interesting and unusual though they undoubtedly are! ITV Westcountry made just the sort of programmes we hoped for. I hope you enjoyed them – and I hope you enjoy this book.

Simon Tonge
Executive Director
Whitley Wildlife Conservation Trust

Opposite page: *Great Grey Owl.*

ACKNOWLEDGEMENTS

The pictures in this book have been taken by many different people. Volunteers, staff members, students and professionals have all contributed images to the Zoo's picture library over the years. In some cases it is impossible to attribute a picture to a named photographer, which is why the acknowledgements have been grouped in this way.

Those we are able to credit include Simon Wootton, Kelvin Halloran, Alasdair McPhee (Miracle Photography), Leza Wills (Paignton Zoo IT Coordinator), Philip Knowling (Paignton Zoo Press Officer), Brian Raynes (Senior Mammal Keeper, Paignton Zoo) and Michelle Turton (Newquay Zoo Marketing Manager). Thanks also to APEX Photo Agency, Andy Styles and Zoo members Ray and Jean Wiltshire for donating images. The picture of the Princess Royal at the official opening of Living Coasts was taken by Steve Pope for the *Herald Express* newspaper. Thanks to the numerous unnamed others for their contributions.

Opposite page: *Male mandrill, Paignton Zoo.*

INTRODUCTION

Zoo Story is a fascinating television documentary series made by ITV Westcountry. The subject of the programmes is the Whitley Wildlife Conservation Trust. This may not be a familiar name in itself, but when you consider that the Trust owns Paignton Zoo Environmental Park, Living Coasts, Slapton Ley and other nature reserves in Devon, and Newquay Zoo in Cornwall, you realise its importance.

Together these conservation attractions welcome nearly one million visitors every year and put huge sums into conservation work both in the UK and abroad. This makes the Whitley Wildlife Conservation Trust one of the South West's leading conservation bodies.

Zoo Story goes behind the scenes to catch a glimpse of the work the public never sees. Visitors may already have some idea that there's more to Paignton (one of Britain's leading zoos) than amazing animals. They may not realise that Paignton has one of the most active zoo science departments in Europe; funds conservation work at home as well as abroad; and maintains local nature reserves. Newquay Zoo has strong education links in the community and operates a local wildlife rescue centre.

A look behind the scenes of any organisation yields surprises. The surprise here is the sheer diversity of work. A modern zoo employs an extraordinary range of people. Everybody knows that a zoo needs zoo-keepers – but at Paignton Zoo there are also ecologists, carpenters, chefs, cleaners, zoologists, shop assistants, gardeners, secretaries, graphic designers and teachers.

Opposite page: Golden lion tamarins live free-range at Paignton Zoo.

Clathrus ruber *fungus in Primley Woods. This extraordinary fungus bursts out of an egg-like case, looking – and smelling – like rotting meat in order to attract flies to carry its spores.*

Beech monolith, Primley Woods nature reserve, Paignton. The reserve is owned by the Whitley Wildlife Conservation Trust and managed by warden Dave Ellacott. Dead wood like this makes excellent habitat for birds, insects, fungi and other organisms.

THE GLOBAL ZOO

The attractions that make up the Whitley Wildlife Conservation Trust family are part of the global zoo. The best zoos worldwide are linked to form what is in effect a single conservation organism. National and international associations coordinate fundraising activities, conservation projects and breeding programmes for endangered species, share best practice on zoo design and animal husbandry, and set the highest standards in education and welfare.

Animals are moved around the world to maintain the genetic viability of captive animal populations and to avoid inbreeding. It's likely that in the not so distant future rare species will exist only in the global zoo. That's why zoos actively support efforts to conserve habitat as well as species. There can be no wild species without wild habitat. Zoos are no substitute for the wild world, but as many habitats decline with frightening speed, zoos find themselves the last refuge for the world's endangered creatures.

Zoo Story shows us the modern zoo. The work is amazing, difficult, uplifting and vitally important. The people are dedicated, knowledgeable and maintain a sense of humour even in the darkest moments. This book is dedicated to everyone who has contributed to the success of the Whitley Wildlife Conservation Trust through the years, from trustees and administrators to staff, volunteers and the visitors who make everything possible. Thank you.

 Paignton Zoo receives over 460 000 visitors a year. Easter Monday 2004 was one of the busiest days ever, with 5154 visitors.

Paignton Zoo Curator of Plants and Gardens Ian Turner guides the removal of a nest of rare wood ants (Formica exsecta) from Paignton Zoo. The nest, rescued from Bovey Heath and removed to Paignton Zoo in 1997, was returned to its former home in 2004 after Devon Wildlife Trust turned the area into a nature reserve.

Below: A TV cameraman films during the move of the rare ant's nest, February 2004.

The Whitley Wildlife Conservation Trust owns and cares for the Primley Woods nature reserve, a mixture of woodland and meadow open to the public.

Opposite page: Blyth's hornbill, Paignton Zoo.

Curator of Plants and Gardens Ian Turner with a stalk of Bromus interruptus, a grass extinct in the wild. Paignton Zoo has contributed seeds to the Millennium Seed Bank.

Above: *Paignton Zoo's miniature train and a young admirer.*

Left: *Female Asiatic lion Jamna with cubs Indu and Sohan and their admiring public, Paignton Zoo, December 2003.*

Opposite page: *Juvenile baboon with pinata.*

15

The Mediterranean garden outside Paignton Zoo's restaurant, May 2004.

Gardens staff work on the new Mediterranean garden near the restaurant, Paignton Zoo, March 2004.

All birds have feathers and everything with feathers is a bird. The ruby hummingbird (*Archilochus colubris*) has just 940 feathers, while the whistling swan (Cygnus columbianus) can have as many as 25 000.

Opposite page: *The Mediterranean garden.*

THE WHITLEY STORY

Herbert Whitley.

Paignton Zoo was founded by Herbert Whitley. He was the archetypal eccentric millionaire, but this shy and unkempt man started what has become one of the most important conservation charities in the South West of England.

THE EARLY YEARS

Herbert Whitley was always mad about animals. When he was small his mother gave him a pair of canaries. He went on to breed and exhibit finches, rabbits, poultry and pigeons – and to found what has become one of the most important zoos in the country.

Opposite page: *Elephants Duchess (left) and Gay, Paignton Zoo.*

Old tropical house, Paignton Zoo.

Herbert Whitley was born in 1886. The Whitley family came to Paignton from Liverpool in 1904. Herbert formed a partnership with his brother William and together they created a breeding centre for a complete range of pedigree livestock. Exotic animals soon followed, including monkeys and cockatoos. Herbert also showed early concerns for the conservation of the world's rare and threatened domestic breeds, keeping Jacob spotted sheep and a zebu, the sacred cow of India – wild, not domestic.

In 1921 Herbert bought Slapton Ley, a freshwater lake 20 miles from Paignton, to save it from commercial exploitation. Later, the conservation of threatened wild species became important to him, too.

THE ZOO OPENS

In 1923 Herbert Whitley opened his collection, then known as Torbay Zoological Gardens, to the public. On show were bears, monkeys, bison, zebra, hyena, baboons and many birds. The entry fee was one shilling (5p) for adults and sixpence (2.5p) for children.

The Zoo had not long been opened before it closed for a period in 1924 due to the implementation of Entertainment Tax. Whitley felt very strongly that his collection was a place of learning and not entertainment.

1930 was a landmark in the Zoo's history. The collection changed its name to Primley Zoological Gardens and the first guidebook was produced. In 1934, the Zoo's tropical house opened to the public.

In 1937, with World War Two looming, the Government decided to close Chessington Zoo in the interest of public safety. Dangerous animals were moved to Paignton, and in 1940 the collection at Paignton was renamed Devon's Zoo and Circus.

Opposite page: Paignton Zoo old entrance, 1970s.

The view across the Zoo towards Primley from above the existing ostrich paddock, c.1950.

Among the additions were a lioness and her four cubs, as well as Peggy, the daughter of tigress, Beauty, star of the film 'Elephant Boy'. The miniature railway added a new dimension to the Zoo, enabling visitors to encircle the Primley lakes.

In 1946 Chessington re-opened. Herbert Whitley then started a partnership with Norman Dixon, a chartered accountant and keen aviculturalist, and the name was changed to Paignton Zoo and Botanical Gardens.

1949 was the year of the elephant, when Paignton Zoo took on two female elephants called Hospie and Jumbo. Their arrival coincided with a new jumbo Zoo guidebook.

In 1955, Whitley's health started to fail. After a long and painful illness he died on 15 September 1955, aged 69. This made headline news. He was buried in a family grave at St Peter's Church, in the thatched village of Buckland-in-the-Moor high on Dartmoor, among the wildlife and countryside he loved.

He left much of his estate to Philip Michelmore, an old friend, colleague and an agriculturalist who spent many years in Africa. His will stipulated that a

Opposite page: Meerkats at Paignton Zoo, April 2004.

Paignton Zoo's female elephants Duchess (African) and Gay (Asian) play together.

Above: *Old subtropical house and walk-through aviary, Paignton Zoo.*

Right: *The old penguin pool and the entrance to what was then the 'Paignton Zoo Quest' interpretation centre, c.1970.*

scientific and educational trust was to be established. The library of books that Herbert had collected was donated to the trust by his nieces and nephews. The trust agreed an arrangement with the Field Studies Council for them to manage Slapton Ley as a nature reserve.

A panel was formed to develop education at the Zoo with Devon County Education Committee and in 1961 a full-time Education Officer, J.I. Menzies, was appointed. Also in 1961, W.E. Francis was appointed as general manager. In 1962 346 751 people visited the Zoo. By 1963 this had risen to 353 849.

In 1968 the first giraffes arrived, and in 1972 the first baby giraffe was born.

In 1973 Rodent City was built and Baboon Rock was opened. In 1976, eleven years after Hospie's death, Jumbo the elephant died. The following year an African elephant called Duchess and an Asian elephant called Gay arrived from Longleat.

Another new attraction, the Ark, opened in 1984 as a family activity centre – this has since been redeveloped as a hands-on educational area. The rhino house was opened in 1986 with the Island Restaurant being completed in 1989. The latter has proved to be a very successful asset to the Zoo.

1993 saw some important new arrivals, with the first orang utans coming from London Zoo. 1995 was a big year in the Zoo's history when the European Regional Development Fund awarded a grant of £2.9 million. For the next six years, major redevelopment was undertaken at Paignton Zoo. In all over £7m was spent modernising the facilities.

Plumed basilisk.

In 1996 the Zoo's name was changed again to Paignton Zoo Environmental Park and the habitat theme was introduced. This started with the forest habitat where the big cats can be seen, the wetland area including flamingo lagoon, and the desert glasshouse.

Apex – Guy Newman

Great Grey Owl.

In 1997 the Marie Le Fevre Ape Centre was added with the arrival of four bachelor gorillas, and the savannah habitat was added with the completion of the elephant and giraffe house.

During this period of redevelopment the Zoo celebrated its 75th anniversary in 1998 – this coincided with the Zoo's first Asiatic lion cubs being born. In 2000, Reptile Tropics, the Zoo's huge hothouse, featuring plants and reptiles from the world's tropical forest, opened to the public.

The new millennium has seen further development of the Zoo with the introduction of new enclosures for cheetah, bongo and mandrill. Other new features have included the Animal Encounters theatre and the Veterinary Centre, a wonderful new facility to ensure the best possible health care for the Zoo's animals.

2003 saw the most ambitious move by the Whitley Wildlife Conservation Trust yet – the opening of Living Coasts, a £7m marine aviary at the heart of Torquay's bustling sea-front. On top of that the Trust purchased Newquay Zoo in Cornwall, reinforcing the charity's position as one of the region's most important conservation bodies.

Only a snippet of Paignton Zoo's history is included here. You can read all about this remarkable collection and its founder, Herbert Whitley, in the book *Chimps, Champs and Elephants* by Jack Baker, on sale at the Zoo.

The giant bamboo (*Gigantochloa verticillata*), to be found in the Zoo's tropical house, can grow at a rate of up to 80cm per night. It only grows during the hours of darkness, which gives it a potential rate of 1mm every 36 seconds.

A BRIEF HISTORY OF PAIGNTON ZOO

1923 Zoo opens to the public
Founded by shy, eccentric millionaire Herbert Whitley. Torbay Zoological Gardens, as it was known then, included monkeys, bison, zebras, baboons and many birds. Entry was one shilling for adults and sixpence for children. From the earliest times education, conservation and botanical themes were important.

1924 Temporary closure
Herbert Whitley had a dispute with the taxman over the imposition of Entertainment Tax – he felt strongly that the zoo was a place of learning and not merely entertainment.

1930 Becomes Primley Zoological Gardens

1934 First Tropical House opens

1940 Paignton takes in war-time evacuees – animals and keepers from Chessington Zoo.

1946 Name changes to Paignton Zoological & Botanical Gardens

1949 First elephants

1955 Herbert Whitley died. The Whitley Wildlife Conservation Trust formed.

1961 Devon Zoology Centre opens

1963 Gibbon Island built

1964 Paignton Zoo becomes a registered charity

1968 First giraffes arrive

1973 Rodent Citiy and Baboon Rock created

1977 Two elephants arrive from Longleat – Duchess (African) and Gay (Asian)

1984 The Ark opens as a family activity centre – this has since been redeveloped as a hands-on educational area.

1986 New rhino house completed

1989 The Island Restaurant opens

1993 The first orang utans arrive (from London Zoo)

1995 £2.9 million grant from European Regional Development Fund; £7m redevelopment starts

1996 Name changes to Paignton Zoo Environmental Park. Habitats theme introduced. Desert House completed

1997 The Marie Le Fevre Ape Centre opens, Savannah opens

1998 Zoo celebrates its 75th Anniversary – this coincides with the Zoo's first Asiatic lion cubs being born. Education centre opened

1999 Avian Breeding Centre completed

2000 Reptile tropics opens; Executive Director Peter Stevens retires and Simon Tonge takes over

2001 Animal Encounters theatre completed; Zoo temporarily closed during Foot and Mouth crisis

2002 Veterinary Centre opens

2003 Living Coasts marine aviary opens in Torquay; Reptile Nursery opens. Mammal Conservation Centre started

2004 TV documentary series on the work of the Whitley Wildlife Conservation Trust

WHAT ARE ZOOS FOR?

A zoo is a great place for a family visit – but there's more to zoos than you might think. One of the most important jobs of a modern zoo is education. It is vital to inform and inspire future generations. The zoo keepers and naturalists of today were raised on childhood trips to the zoo. Thousands of children come to Paignton Zoo, Living Coasts and Newquay Zoo on organised trips every year.

Education is one of the most high-profile tasks of any zoo. However, there is – quite literally – more to zoos than meets the eye. Behind the scenes our top zoos are working on scientific research projects, species and habitat conservation schemes, both at home and abroad, along with the breeding of rare and endangered animals.

Zoos get people up close to animals they would never otherwise see. They help to raise awareness for wildlife and conservation issues. They tell us about the wonders of far away places – they help us connect with the natural world.

Paignton Zoo has 75 acres of parkland and gardens and is home to hundreds of rare and exotic plants, birds, mammals and reptiles. In addition there's a restaurant, shop and plenty of entertainment for children of all ages. It's a great day out. But zoos do a lot more.

Everyone who visits Paignton Zoo is supporting local, national and international conservation work. Entrance fees go towards the care of the plants and animals in the collection and support conservation and scientific research work. The zoo is where global conservation enters the mainstream.

Young people enjoy activities around Paignton Zoo with the Gibbon Club

Opposite page: Mapema, male western lowland gorilla, Paignton Zoo.

29

Top modern establishments like Paignton do not work alone. Paignton is part of a global zoo. Animals are moved around the world to keep the gene pools of captive populations fresh and to prevent inbreeding. The work is carefully coordinated and detailed records are kept. Throughout all of this, the care and welfare of the animals is paramount. Zoos also carry out scientific research into animal welfare, enrichment, husbandry and nutrition issues.

Paignton Zoo conducts conservation work both here and abroad. In this country staff and students investigate everything from rare thistles and moths to dormice and water voles. Work in Nigeria, Zimbabwe, Malawi and South Africa is helping black rhino, cheetah, antelope and elephant.

Zoos are busy places both publicly and behind the scenes. It's the support of the public that helps to fund the vital behind-the-scenes work.

Above: *Jungle bridge, Paignton Zoo.*

Right: *Paignton Zoo's female Sumatran tiger Banda.*

Opposite page: *Crowds stroll through the wooded grounds.*

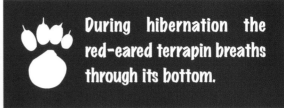

During hibernation the red-eared terrapin breaths through its bottom.

Above: *Grrrrr!*

Top left: *Western grey kangaroo and offspring, Paignton Zoo, 2004.*

Left: *Nose to nose with Jamna, Paignton's Asiatic lioness.*

Opposite page: *View over the new mammal centre towards the elephant house, Paignton Zoo, May 2004.*

Right: *Paignton Zoo's gorilla island on a misty spring morning.*

Below: *Radiographer Neil Pierce (left) and Farrier Robbie Richardson.*

Nearly 50 000 children and students come to Paignton Zoo on organised visits every year

Whitley Wildlife Conservation Trust reserves warden Dave Ellacott takes a school group pond dipping.

Paignton Zoo mammal keeper Emma Gilchrist and black rhino Kingo.

Right: *Midas and Jamna the Asiatic lions.*

Below: *Abbysinian Ground Hornbill.*

Scarlet Ibis.

Above: *Spring blossom on a Japanese crab apple in the grounds of Paignton Zoo.*

Right: *Looking across the lake to Gibbon island, Paignton Zoo.*

Below: *Autumn foliage at Paignton Zoo.*

ZOO SCIENCE

The quality of research work both at home and in the field has gained Paignton Zoo and the Whitley Wildlife Conservation Trust an international reputation.

Paignton Zoo has what is probably the biggest zoo-based research team in Europe with six permanent staff members, including a unique joint appointment with a university. As well as over 60 zoo-based research projects each year, this team runs or supports more than 20 conservation projects in the field, ranging from meadow thistles and water shrews in Devon, to black rhino in Malawi and rare antelope in Zimbabwe.

The emphasis on science goes back to the founding principles of Herbert Whitley. Dr Amy Plowman was appointed as Science Officer at Paignton Zoo in 1997 to launch a new-style Science Department. Since then the Whitley Wildlife Conservation Trust has spent something in the region of £400 000 on conservation and research work.

Amy is now Head of Science for Paignton Zoo, Living Coasts and Newquay Zoo. The department has been expanding rapidly since 2001 (when the first zoo-funded PhD placement was taken on) and is now one of the biggest and busiest in Europe with eight industrial year placement students working alongside the permanent staff.

A unique partnership to employ a joint member of staff with The University of Exeter began in 2003. Department staff teach on an MSc in Animal Behaviour at Exeter. A new MSc in Zoo Conservation Biology has been jointly

Asian elephant Gay plays with a ball made of old hosepipe donated by the local fire brigade. The ball contains food and stimulates play activity

Opposite page: Sumatran tiger, Paignton Zoo.

Since the launch of the Paignton Zoo Science Department in 1997 staff have initiated and supervised over 300 research projects undertaken by students ranging from A level to PhD from colleges in the UK and abroad.

developed and is being jointly delivered by zoo staff and the University of Plymouth.

Between 1997 and 2004 the Department wrote over 60 scientific articles, including 12 peer-reviewed journal papers, and made over 80 scientific conference presentations. This makes Paignton one of the most scientifically prolific zoos in Europe, if not the world. The research work at Paignton Zoo covers a huge range: from applied animal behaviour and welfare, animal cognition and psychology to behavioural ecology, nutrition, parasitology, genetics and environmental science.

Stepping out at Paignton Zoo, a young Cassowary follows its keeper.

Members of the Paignton Zoo Science Department – Dr Vicky Melfi, D Amy Plowman, Natasha DeVere, Dr Christine Caldwell, Kirsten Pullen.

Opposite page: *Mammal keeper Louise Hector provides enrichment for the anoa, a species of miniature water buffalo.*

STUDENTS

Staff supervise over 60 student projects every year at Paignton Zoo and Living Coasts, with many placements from universities in Plymouth, Exeter, Cardiff and Manchester. Students have also come from the Van Hall Institute in Holland, the Free University of Berlin, the University of West Australia and Michigan State University (USA). Newquay Zoo has formed a strong partnership with the Centre for Applied Zoology (part of Cornwall College and the Combined Universities in Cornwall) and works closely with their students on various projects.

Paignton Zoo is now conducting science work for other zoos through its not-for-profit Research Services Consultancy. Many zoos cannot afford to employ staff with the necessary research skills, so Paignton helps these zoos to develop a high-quality scientific research programme, trains staff and/or students to do the research and assists in report writing and presentation.

FIELD RESEARCH AND CONSERVATION

Delegates at the Primate Society of Great Britain Easter meeting, Paignton Zoo 2004.

The Whitley Wildlife Conservation Trust has made huge investments in field conservation. In this country the Trust owns and manages the Primley and Clennon nature reserves in Paignton and also owns Slapton Ley (managed by English Nature and the Field Studies Council).

Paignton Zoo is active in Zimbabwe, Zanzibar, Kenya, Nigeria, Malawi and Botswana. Living Coasts is forming links with marine conservation organisations at home and abroad.

Newquay Zoo supports field projects in Vietnam and Colombia, funds research into penguins and fossa, and has formed a strong partnership with the Centre for Applied Zoology (part of Cornwall College and the Combined Universities in Cornwall).

Male cheetah Cado investigates a traffic cone during a study into cheetah character types.

ZOO STORY ON TELEVISION

ITV Westcountry made the Zoo Story programmes about the work of the Whitley Wildlife Conservation Trust and its growing family of conservation organisations, including Paignton Zoo, Living Coasts, Slapton Ley and Newquay Zoo.

After three highly successful years with Country Lives, producer Grace Kitto was keen to ring the changes with a new animal-based series. Grace: "I looked at animal sanctuaries and wildlife themes and various other things – but I was immediately struck by the possibilities of the Zoo. It is internationally famous, one of the top zoos in the country, and nothing had been done on it for years. Taking into account that it now has offshoots at Living Coasts and Slapton Ley, and has recently taken over the running of Newquay Zoo, I thought there was a lot of mileage for a behind-the-scenes look at the whole Whitely Wildlife Conservation Trust."

She goes on: "The purpose of the series is threefold – to look at events in the animals' lives that you don't see on a day trip; to see the Zoo in its international context, concerned with science and conservation; and to use the camera to the full so that you see in close-up in a way that you can't do in person."

Film crews usually shoot about ten times the footage they need, which means that the team had something like 50 hours of video tape by the time they came to edit the first series. The first five programmes feature everything from the treatment of a limping lion cub and hand-rearing a giraffe to environmental enrichment work and the life cycle of cassowaries. The first series of Zoo Story was broadcast in July 2004, and the second in December 2004.

Opposite page:
A rare flap-necked chameleon born at Paignton Zoo from parents confiscated by customs officers at Heathrow airport.

Opposite page: *Documentary team Left to right: Pete Underwood (sound), Leila Fletcher (researcher), Grace Kitto (producer and director), Chris Topliss (cameras).*

Right: *Interviewing staff during Zoolu's departure from Paignton Zoo, May 2004.*

Below: *Paignton Zoo's male Sumatran tiger, Tenang.*

Filming with elephant keeper Jim Dicks.

Asiatic lion cubs Indu and Sohan at a couple of months, 2004.

Photographs by Andy Styles

Red Ruffed Lemurs.

49

SO YOU WANT TO BE A ZOO KEEPER?

The role of zoo keeper is one of the most popular jobs involving animals. Keepers have a responsibility both to the animals in their care and to the general public. Working in an animal collection is a question of balancing the needs of the animals and the visitors' desire for information.

You want to be a zoo keeper – but are you cut out for a career in zoos? Your love of animals must not be sentimental – you may have to care for sick or injured animals. However, if you have enthusiasm, commitment and knowledge, working with them can be very rewarding.

Zoo work is demanding. Animal-keeping staff often work at weekends and hours are long. Working with animals is often dirty, mundane and physically demanding. Employers look for people with stamina and commitment, as well as a love for and knowledge of animals.

A keeper's routine involves cleaning enclosures, preparing food, providing fresh water and clean bedding and ensuring that animal enclosures are kept at the appropriate temperature and humidity. They also keep records on health, diet and the behaviour of the animals in their care and assist the vet when either preventative or curative treatment is needed.

You need to have good communication skills. Dealing with people – visitors and zoo professionals – as well as animals is part of the job. There can be a lot of contact with zoo visitors – after the animals it is the keepers that the public like to see. In the majority of zoos, keepers are an essential part of public education programmes, giving talks and participating in and organising events and activities for school groups and other interested parties.

Paignton Zoo elephant keeper Amanda Hendy hands out stickers

Opposite page: *Paignton Zoo's Asiatic lions, female Jamna and male Midas*

Entry qualifications can vary from collection to collection. Many require five GCSEs, including a natural science (such as biology), maths and English. Many zoo keepers now have a relevant university degree. However, experience is important, too – evidence of voluntary work and summer jobs with animals always helps.

Initially, training is done on-the-job and given by other qualified members of staff. Having completed a six month probationary period, most zoos require keepers to study and obtain a City and Guilds Advanced National Certificate in Management of Zoo Animals by taking a distance learning course through the Sparsholt College.

If you wish to apply to be a keeper at Paignton Zoo, write to the appropriate curator – there is no application form. Give details of your experience and qualifications and remember to include an SAE. Zoo keeping jobs are in great demand, but for the right person it's the best job in the world.

Above: *Baby Baboon*

Right: *Keeper Jim Dicks and the Paignton Zoo giraffes.*

Opposite page: *Paignton Zoo senior reptile keeper Katie Clegg with giant tortoise.*

Apex – Chris Saville

Mammal keeper Jean Lee prepares food at Christmas. Animals need looking after every day of the year, which means some keepers have to work even on Christmas Day.

Top left: *Devika the Asian Lion cub gets a feed from Paignton Zoo keeper Jason Knight.*

Left: *Mammal keepers Amanda Hendy, Julian Chapman and Robert Rouse in a fire engine, January 2004. Devon Fire & Rescue Service donates old hoses to Paignton Zoo for use in enrichment work. You can make everything from elephant footballs to baboon hammocks out of old hosepipe.*

Baboon Rock.

Above: *Zoo keeper Jason Knight.*

Top left: *Snake encounter.*

Left: *A keeper's day features a lot of cleaning, feeding and watering.*

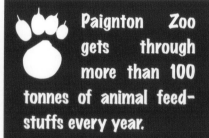

Paignton Zoo gets through more than 100 tonnes of animal feed-stuffs every year.

Opposite page: *Bird keeper Peter Smallbones takes a hand-reared cassowary chick for a walk.*

NEWQUAY ZOO

Newquay Zoo was founded in 1969 by the local council and extensively modernised under private ownership in the 1990s. In 2003 it was purchased by the Whitley Wildlife Conservation Trust. The tranquil ten-acre lakeside gardens on the edge of the bustling coastal resort of Newquay are home to a wide range of rare and endangered animals from habitats all around the world.

Awards have been won for education, tourism, sustainable development, research and animal welfare, including innovative mixed-species enclosures such as the African Plains. Another unusual feature is research into the use of alternative remedies such as homeopathy in animal health and rehabilitation. Plans are in place to develop this facility where Wendy Winstanley, Wildlife Hospital Manager, cares for injured British wildlife in the Zoos Wildlife Hospital, whilst also coordinating the North Cornwall Bat Rescue Centre.

Recent exciting redevelopments include the refurbished Oriental Garden and the rainforest aviary in the Tropical House. In this steamy, humid, tropical rainforest environment, water cascades down ancient temple walls to jungle pools, home to turtles and fish. Tropical birds and small mammals may be glimpsed coming to drink. After looking out at treetop level for sloths and flying fox fruit bats, visitors explore life in the undergrowth in our minibeast area (including a new poison arrow frog enclosure), before setting off to view other endangered rainforest animals including the Tamandua (lesser ant-eater) in the nocturnal house. Amongst the sub-tropical lakeside gardens live hundreds of animals from all around the world, ranging from small rare monkeys to shy red pandas. Look out for meerkats on sentry duty, penguins playing in their pool, and glimpse

Opposite page: *Red panda.*

59

the strange and endangered lemurs and fossa. Highlights of the day include feeding-time talks and the animal encounters where you can meet keepers and some of the animals.

There are plans to expand the zoo on to adjoining land to include an education and environment interpretation centre and new visitor facilities in a landscaped African savannah enclosure of about three acres. Assistant Director Stewart Muir said 'We are designing this new African area as a mixed-species exhibit built around a waterhole. It will include a range of species new to the zoo, as well as a sustainably-built complex to house new educational, conference and catering facilities.' Funding for this exciting development is being sought from European Union Objective One funds, the South West Regional Development Agency, local councils and other funding bodies.

Opposite page: Newquay Zoo Assistant Director Stewart Muir in the tropical house.

Two mara or Patagonian cavy free-ranging in the grounds of Newquay Zoo.

A strong, award-winning partnership exists between Newquay Zoo and the Centre for Applied Zoology (part of Cornwall College and the Combined Universities in Cornwall) offering conservation and marine courses at BTEC and degree level. Students receive a practical and vocational element to their course through involvement in many aspects of zoo life. Zoo staff from management, finance, education and animal sections form part of the teaching team. For information on these courses, visit www.cornwall.ac.uk.

Newquay Zoo education officer Mark Norris talking to visitors.

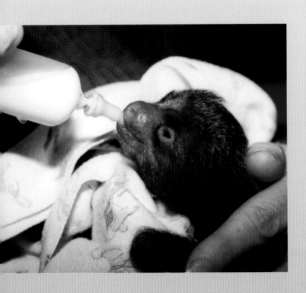

Left: *Roxy Peru – born to mum Bottoms Up and dad Slow Joe (pictured above) at Newquay Zoo on 31st December 2001; she was rejected and had to be handreared. Newquay Zoo has won awards for its work with Hoffmann's Sloths and its support for Sloth rehabilitation projects in Colombia.*

Above: *Red panda, Newquay Zoo.*

Right: *Ring-tailed lemurs at Newquay Zoo get to know their keeper.*

On a summer day a large oak tree may take up a hundred gallons of water or more; a large beech tree can provide enough oxygen for the daily requirement of ten people.

LIVING COASTS
Life on the Edge

Her Royal Highness the Princess Royal during the official opening of Living Coasts, September 2003.

Opposite page: A fur seal seen through the viewing dome at Living Coasts.

Living Coasts is the most ambitious project the Whitley Wildlife Conservation Trust has ever undertaken. The marine aviary on the Torquay waterfront allows visitors to get up close to penguins, puffins, fur seals, wading birds and sea ducks, all immersed in an environment landscaped with rocks and plants under a vast tent-like canopy. They can watch species both on and under the water, and afterwards relax in the restaurant with its unbeatable views across Tor Bay.

The attraction's slogan – Life on the Edge – is fitting. Living Coasts is all about the plants, animals and habitats that make up that thin margin between land and sea. It's also about our own relationship with these areas and the impact of seaside holidays, pollution and development. Living Coasts holds up a magnifying glass to our shorelines.

Designed by world-renowned Torquay practice Kay Elliott Architects, the main contractor was Dean & Dyball of Exeter. The project was part-funded by the European Regional Development Fund and the South West Regional Development Agency.

Living Coasts has a unique silhouette thanks to its see-through net roof, held aloft on special masts. It also boasts an extremely desirable location – very few maritime attractions or aquaria have such a panoramic water's-edge setting. It means you can view local wildlife and unfamiliar species from the same spot.

Living Coasts has become a local landmark.

Happy customers in the Azure restaurant.

Month-old avocet chick, Living Coasts, May 2004.

Project Manager Barry Edwards said: "Of the species and habitats represented, some are here because they are endangered, others because they are extraordinary, and some because they are local but still rarely-seen. Nothing has ever been done with birds in this country on this scale before."

"There is a strong conservation and education element in everything we do. Living Coasts is about raising awareness and encouraging personal action," said Paignton Zoo Executive Director Simon Tonge. "Living Coasts aims to be both exciting and thought-provoking – while the species on show are fascinating and engaging, the underlying message is that we need to respect and understand our coastal habitats."

The construction of Paignton [...] attraction brings to an end a lon[...] Beacon Cove site.

In 1857 the Bath's Saloons wer[...] looking Beacon Cove. They in[...] bathing facilities with, under[...] bath open to the sea. The be[...] bath can still be seen today an[...] into the lower part of the Livi[...]

In 1869 the baths closed an[...] the space. Around the time [...] Spa was built on the site. [...] popular past-time and tou[...] responded by building a m[...] undercover pool. Dances [...]ith swimming compe-titions and galas downstair[...]

By the 1960s the Marine [...]un-down. It was finally demolished in 1971. Co[...] concrete eyesore, it was razed in 1997. After tha[...]n. Many ideas were put forward for the site – ev[...]nton Zoo, the concept of Living Coasts evolved.

With the construction [...]ece in the regeneration of this part of the Torqua[...]ace. There is public access to Beacon Cove once[...] is landscaped to blend in with the natural shore[...]r world-class environmental attraction.

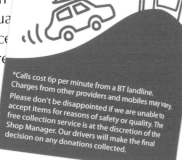

Members of the Paignton Zoo maintenance team in the penguin pool during routine maintenance, Living Coasts, January 2004.

Several keepers at Living Coasts are also trained divers. They enter the pools to clean the glass.

Left: *Construction work, November 2002.*

Below: *The first avocet chick to be hatched at Living Coasts, April 2004.*

In under a year Living Coasts sold over 2000 gallons of tea and coffee. In one year Paignton Zoo's Island Restaurant gets through 70 tonnes of chips.

Right: *View from waders' estuary looking across the seal pool, Living Coasts.*

 Gentoo penguins are the fastest underwater swimming birds and can reach speeds of up to 22mph.

A young fur seal demonstrates gymnastic prowess at Living Coasts.

Gentoo penguin at Living Coasts.

Tufted puffin, Living Coasts.

Top: *Staff at Living Coasts before the opening, July 2003.*

Above: *Operations engineer Glenn Frost in the plant-room at Living Coasts, where state of the art equipment regulates the water quality and clarity.*

Right: *Living Coasts presenter Alex Barron is a shark fanatic!*

Opposite page, clockwise from top left:

Pied avocets on the waders' estuary, Living Coasts.

Workers on one of the pylons at Living Coasts during a routine inspection, April 2004.

A bird sillouetted against the vast net canopy at Living Coasts.

Living Coasts staff lead regular clean-ups on local beaches.

Above: *Three Inca terns, Living Coasts.*

Left: *A spectacled eider.*

FAIRER TRADING

Paignton Zoo and Living Coasts are well-known as tourist attractions. Many people don't realise that they are also registered charities. The trading arm – Paignton Zoo Enterprises – is made up of the catering and retail departments. Profits are covenanted to the parent education and conservation charity, the Whitley Wildlife Conservation Trust.

In 10 years the retail arm alone has raised over £3.2 million for the charity. Under the guidance of Senior Retail Manager Tony Stokes sales have increased faster than visitor numbers. In 1993 retail's contribution to Paignton Zoo Enterprises was £68 261; in 2003 it was £609 474. Sales have increased by 557%, while the retail contribution to the Trust has increased by 756%.

Tony takes a particular interest in the concept of fair trade, which aims to do business without harming the environment or the lives of people in the developing world. The approach is not only ethical – it makes good business sense. In 2004 Paignton Zoo sold over £100 000 worth of items under their Fairer World banner. This is a label Tony Stokes and his team developed to indicate items from ethical or fair trade sources which are environmentally sound.

Tony Stokes says: "Globalisation, exploitation and poverty are thought of as human problems. In fact they can have a devastating impact on wildlife and the environment, too.

"Big businesses source low-cost labour in developing nations to manufacture products for our shelves and turn a blind eye to the misery that this can cause. Workers in factories throughout the developing world face shifts of up to sixteen

Delegates at the Sixth International Zoo Design Symposium, hosted jointly by Paignton Zoo and Living Coasts at the Grand Hotel, Torquay, May 2004. The conference attracted 120 people from 19 countries.

Opposite page: *Black rhinos Sita and Kinso.*

hours a day, seven days a week, often just to earn enough to eat. Five billion people live on less than 2 dollars a day.

"These factories produce for the most developed countries whilst polluting the least developed countries. Pollution and deforestation affect both wildlife and the environment. Thousands of species of plants and animals are under increasing threat."

People unable to follow their traditional way of life often turn to crafts as a means of survival. Workshops sponsored by ethical suppliers help preserve traditional designs and skills passed down through generations.

Black rhino in Zimbabwe, the subject of conservation work by the Whitley Wildlife Conservation Trust.

Unfortunately, few suppliers or small producers in the developing world have a sophisticated marketing facility or a warehouse full of stock available for immediate delivery. In most cases there is a requirement to produce to fulfil advance orders only. Tony Stokes and colleagues – including retail administration manager Anne Wills and Paignton Zoo artist Sue Misselbrook – have been working on a way to collate orders from other zoos to send on to small suppliers.

Tony Stokes says: "Trade is essential to help poor communities develop, but it must be managed so as to be sustainable and beneficial if the goal of long-term change is to be realised. Zoos have the opportunity, both individually and collectively, to make a positive impact by supporting fair trade and ethical suppliers who are engaged in fighting poverty and injustice.

Paignton Zoo is leading the way in ethical trading for zoos across the country. To make things even easier, the Paignton Zoo shop is open to non-visitors so you don't have to pay entry to the Zoo to shop there. The same is true at Living Coasts. Shop on-line at www.paigntonzoo.org.uk.

Ishola and Adomola carry out environmental education work in the Omo Forest, Nigeria, thanks to funding from the Whitley Wildlife Conservation Trust.

A duiker, the rare antelope which is the subject of conservation efforts in Zimbabwe, Kenya and Zanzibar, supported by the Whitley Wildlife Conservation Trust.

BADGER WATCH

When was the last time you spotted a live badger? Sadly, most of us only see them as casualties on the roadside. We know they are out there in the countryside, they pop up in children's stories and the striped face is instantly familiar – but in reality they are elusive creatures.

Somewhat surprisingly, you can watch wild badgers at Paignton Zoo. As well as fascinating plant and animal species from around the world, Paignton Zoo is home to a wide range of British wildlife. Rabbits, buzzards, squirrels and others can be seen by day. By night there are foxes, owls – and badgers.

The Badger Watch at Paignton Zoo runs between April and November on weekday evenings. Groups and individuals and children over 10 are welcome. A visit lasts about two hours – wear sensible clothing and be prepared to sit quietly. There's no guarantee that you will see badgers (though it is rare not to). However, if you don't see any then you receive a free return visit or a full refund.

A badger close up.

THE EVENING

We meet at the front gate of the Zoo after the crowds have gone home. This is a rare opportunity to take a moonlit, black-and-white look into the badger's world. Badgers moved into an old antelope paddock in 1977. The hide was built in 2000 as part of the regeneration of the Zoo. It is set into the side of the hill with its forward-facing windows at ground level. An artificial tunnel runs below these, with three windows inside the hide at floor-level.

Opposite page: *Wild badger in the observation hide, Paignton Zoo.*

Wild badger emerging from a tunnel, Paignton Zoo.

It is plain but comfortable – wooden benches with cushions, a wide wall of windows and a TV monitor showing the view down into one of the many badger holes from a small camera mounted on a post. There are photographs of badgers on the walls, mostly taken by keeper Brian Raynes, who operates Badger Watch.

We settle in, the air thick with anticipation. It's exciting whether or not you have been before – and many people come time and again. The keeper leading the watch puts food out – nuts, cereals and peanut butter. It's just like feeding the wild birds in your garden.

Special lights with tungsten bulbs to give a moonlight effect illuminate the rough grass in front of the hide. The odd call of a maned wolf breaks the evening peace and adds to the sense of occasion.

An early glimpse of a badger nose on the TV monitor raises our excitement, but we have to wait until deep dusk for the badgers to appear. They come out of the leafy shadows, one then two then three, their striped faces surprisingly clear in the grainy gloom. They are big creatures with powerful jaws and well-defined heads. It's hard to believe that they are related to weasels.

Minutes later there's a badger on the other side of the main window, within a metre of us. I realise I'm watching open-mouthed. A female appears in the tunnel – effectively inside the hide. She snuffles and sniffs and emerges into one of the chambers where food has been scattered. She is so close you can hear her crunching and munching on the food. And she can hear us; the movement of a coat makes her stop and look up – but she is not scared away.

We lose all track of time, but the clock ticks on and night falls. Almost on cue the badgers move on and the evening is over. We make our way back through the nocturnal Zoo – the walk itself is a special experience.

Badgers are out in our landscape every night, all over the country. Most of us never see them. This is a thrilling reminder that the natural world never sleeps.

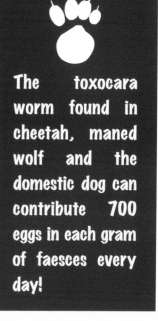

The toxocara worm found in cheetah, maned wolf and the domestic dog can contribute 700 eggs in each gram of faesces every day!

Wild badger pictured during an evening Badger Watch in the grounds of Paignton Zoo.

ZOOLU

He was one of the most amazing new-borns you could ever imagine. He was delicate and dark eyed and stood – sometimes a little shakily – at something over two metres (6 feet) tall. Zoolu the male Rothschild giraffe was born at Paignton Zoo on Friday 23 May 2003.

Born on a bank holiday weekend, Zoolu was wowing visitors to the Zoo from his first days. He was rejected by his mother and had to be hand-reared by senior keeper Jim Dicks. Over the first few days and weeks Jim would be at the Zoo for 6:00 in the morning and often stay until after 11:00 at night.

The calf was big and strong, weighing in the region of 70kgs (150lbs) at birth, and fed well. The Definitely Devon dairy came to the new-born's aid with supplies of cream and milk. The staff at Definitely Devon were invited to name the youngster, and came up with Zoolu.

By seven months Zoolu was slowly being weaned; he was down to just three feeds of milk a day and had started eating lucerne, browse and fruit. The aim was to move him on after about a year; he couldn't stay with his parents and it's better to move a giraffe before he gets too tall… After much planning and discussion, a place was found for him at Twycross Zoo in Warwickshire, where he could join a herd.

Zoos put a lot of work into maintaining genetically diverse animal populations and avoiding inbreeding. There are international breeding programmes and records are kept in the form of studbooks. Computer software helps keep track of the pedigrees of individual animals and allows studbook coordinators to analyse populations.

Keeper Jim Dicks with Zoolu.

Opposite page: *Giraffe, Paignton Zoo.*

Keeper Amanda Hendy with supplies for Zoolu.

Coordinators produce plans for the future management of species; working with a committee, they make recommendations on which animals should breed or not breed and which individual animals should go where. Collections donate animals or loan them; usually the receiving institution pays the travel costs.

Zoolu left Paignton on 19 May 2004, at almost exactly one year old. He travelled in style in his own made-to-measure first-class compartment. A special crate was built by the Zoo's Maintenance Department. Constructed of heavy duty 50mm square hollow section steel and plywood panelling, it stood 3.6 metres high, 2.4 metres long and 1.8 metres wide. The crate weighed approximately 1 tonne while Zoolu himself weighed a third of a tonne.

The move was very much a team effort. The day was planned by Curator of Mammals Neil Bemment and supervised by Clerk of Works Adi Board. Maintenance Coordinator Rob Williams used a large tele-handler on free loan from CRMS machinery, based at Heathfield near Newton Abbot, to load the crate and Zoolu onto a low-loader for the journey. The low loader was supplied by Aardvark Haulage.

The process started before 9:00am. The crate had been introduced into the giraffe enclosure at the start of May so all the animals could get used to it. Keeping staff Jim Dicks, Mandy Hendy and Julian Chapman maneuvered Zoolu into it with the minimum of fuss, allowing him to find his own way rather than driving him in.

The crate had an open top covered by a fitted tarpaulin to protect Zoolu from the elements. Keeper Amanda Hendy went with Zoolu to see him settled into his new home. By 10:30am they had set off on the 210 mile journey.

The drive to Twycross went smoothly, apart from a ripped tarpaulin, and Zoolu settled in with extraordinarily speed. In fact he refused his feed the next day because he was already bonding with the other giraffes.

Over the year Definitely Devon dairy donated hundreds of litres of milk and cream. Zoolu was about 2 metres (6 feet) tall and would have weighed in the region of 70kgs (150lbs) when born. At departure he was about 300-350kgs (660 to 770lbs) and 3 metres (10 feet) tall. Male Rothschild giraffes can grow to be 5.5 m (18 ft) and weigh up to 1200 kg (2700 lbs).

Staff and visitors alike were sorry to see Zoolu go as he had become a very popular character. It's especially hard for keeping staff, who have invested so much time and effort in an animal, to see it move on. But, as always, it is what is best for the animal that counts.

The move begins.

Apex – Mark Passmore

Zoolu, born to mother Kizi & father Paddy.

Paddy, Paignton Zoo's male Rothschild giraffe.

There are now 10 000 PAWS members - Zoo supporters.

Opposite page,
clockwise from top left:

Zoolu's travelling crate is moved through the Zoo to the giraffe house.

Jim Dicks says goodbye.

Through the back gate of the Zoo.

ZOO VET

Vet Ghislaine Sayers started work at Paignton Zoo in May 2000. By then Paignton had become big enough and was of a high enough calibre to warrant a dedicated vet and veterinary facility on site. Prior to that a local practice vet would be called in to treat sick Zoo animals.

The aim of the new department was to improve the way the Zoo kept its animals by learning more about them and the diseases they had. This emphasis on preventative medicine was down to then-Executive Director Peter Stevens.

It is a common belief that disease is caused by bacteria, viruses or some other infectious entity. In reality disease can be caused by such things as sub-optimal nutrition, sub-optimal housing, incorrect group size or age and sex ratios, inclement weather or a lack of opportunity to perform normal behaviours – or any combination of these.

Ghislaine's first job was to design a vet centre and source the equipment to provide a veterinary service for all the animals at the Zoo. This was a fantastic opportunity to start a project from scratch. In November 2001 staff moved into the new vet centre and in July 2002 it was officially opened by Noel Edmunds. None of this would have been possible without funding from the Whitley Wildlife Conservation Trust or the help of Peter Stevens and the many sponsors who provided support or equipment. Today the vet centre consists of an operating room, radiography room, recovery and hospitalisation areas, post-mortem room, pharmacy and offices.

Paignton Zoo vet Ghislaine Sayers armed with a tranquiliser gun.

Opposite page: *Burmese Python, Paignton Zoo.*

Specialists: Radiographer (left) and Farrier (right).

What started with one person has increased to a team of three. Sheona McGovern and Kelly Elford are full time registered and qualified veterinary nurses; Sheona also has a certificate in exotics nursing and has worked in referral practices and Dublin vet school, while Kelly has an interest in lab work and does routine faecal screening. The nurses monitor anaesthesia, dispense and administer treatments, prepare, clean and maintain equipment, take radiographs, work in the lab, help with post-mortems and do a lot of the administrative work.

Ghislaine became a zoo vet through a combination of training, experience and being in the right place at the right time. After qualifying she worked in general practice for three years, getting a basic grounding in all aspects of clinical and surgical work.

Veterinary officer Ghislaine Sayers and vet nurse Sheona McGovern watched by visitors.

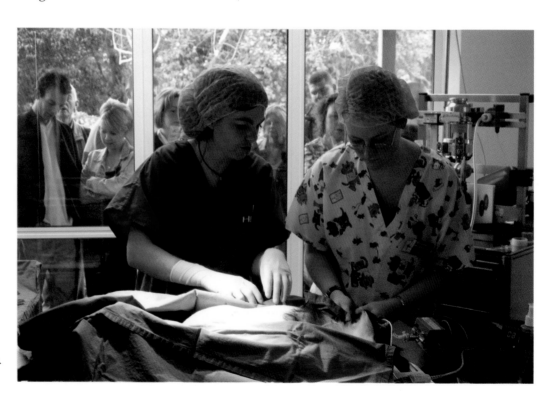

She had always wanted to do conservation medicine and had the opportunity to go to South Africa to do a wildlife immobilisation course. From here she gave up her job and went back to University to take an MSc in wild animal health based at London Zoo. This gave her an opportunity to meet other people who were doing conservation research and to work on research projects. The first was investigating mydriatics in terrapins in the UK and the second was in the Serengeti. She spent a year working with her husband on the demography and behaviour of cheetahs. This was part of a larger project to find minimum viable population sizes of cheetahs in the Serengeti National Park. It was an amazing year and a hard act to follow. When she came back to England she worked for two years in a wildlife hospital and rehabilitation centre before coming to work at Paignton.

Paignton Zoo vet Ghislaine Sayers with a tapir.

The aim of Paignton Zoo's vet department is to maximise animal welfare. The staff treat sick animals but it is just as important to try and prevent animals from becoming sick in the first place. This can be done by screening for disease at different stages and when disease is found, by investigating the causes.

The first step is to stop disease from coming into the Zoo with new animals. As so many animals are involved in conservation breeding programmes it is important to check that they are healthy before they travel. Most wild animals are very good at hiding signs of disease until the problem is quite advanced. By screening for disease, problems can be picked up early. This stops animals travelling while they are sick, which can cause stress.

Hartmann's mountain zebras, Paignton Zoo.

Change can be stressful for animals and cause the immune system to be suppressed. When an animal arrives at its new home it needs to cope with changes in routine, habitat, enclosure and companions. It is common for clinical signs of disease to be seen at this time, so it is important to keep screening.

Twice a year all the animals at Paignton Zoo are screened for parasites and there is a worming programme to prevent the build up of parasites. Staff also need to check for zoonoses – diseases which can be transmitted from animals to humans such as tuberculosis or salmonella. If an animal is anaesthetised for any reason Ghislaine takes the opportunity to find out as much about it as possible. This may include finding out what is normal so there is information to refer to if the animal becomes sick.

Farrier Robbie Richardson, curator of mammals Neil Belment and keeper Brian Raynes examine a zebra's hoof.

At one of these health screens staff commonly take blood samples to look at blood cells, biochemistry to check for organ damage, serology to look for exposure to viruses, carry out dental checks including tooth cleaning, take radiographs to check for lung, heart and liver disease and do a thorough clinical examination. Animals are often transponded with microchips so they can be permanently identified.

Dental disease and abnormal hoof growth can occur in all animals, so part of the veterinary department's job is to treat these problems when they occur. If problems increase staff need to investigate by, for instance, looking at the animals' diet and the substrate the animals are walking on. These types of investigations are often a team effort involving several Zoo departments and sometimes outside consultants. Paignton Zoo employs people with specialised knowledge and years of experience who are all working for the good of the animals. Pooling their knowledge and looking at problems from different angles achieves far more than working in isolation.

Many animals can be prone to diseases for which they show no clinical signs in the early stages (sub-clinical diseases). Post-mortems are an ideal opportunity to find out why an animal died and whether sub-clinical diseases were present. By analysing findings Ghislaine can begin to see potential problems with diet, particular infectious agents or husbandry routines. Post-mortems allow staff to address problems and prevent diseases in other animals; for that reason, a

Left: *Zebra, Paignton Zoo.*

Below left: *Keepers, vet staff and medical experts on hand during an ultrasound scan of a gorilla.*

Below right: *Checking on the anaesthatised Western lowland gorilla Rick during his move from Paignton to Prague, November 2003.*

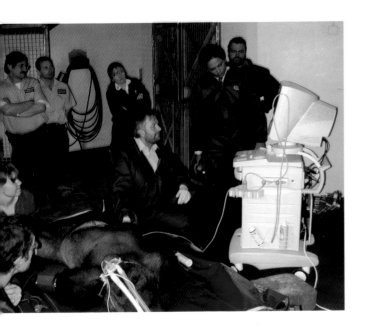

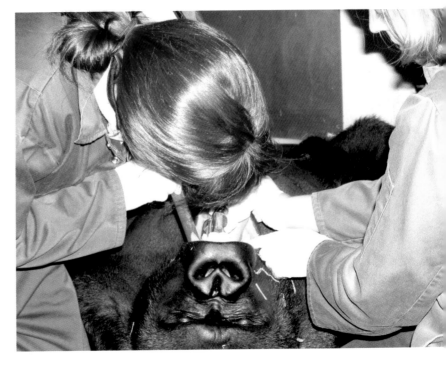

Above: Gambira, juvenile orang utang, Paignton Zoo.

Top left: Cheetah, Paignton Zoo.

Left: Orang utang on one of the
islands at Paignton Zoo.

The Zoo borehole supplies
8000 cubic metres of
water per annum.

post-mortem is carried out on every animal that dies even if the cause of death is known.

One of the aims of Paignton Zoo is to breed endangered species and the veterinary team is involved in this process too. When things don't go according to plan they can help with difficult births (though these are few and far between). Mostly they investigate the medical causes of infertility and try to improve fertility. There are times when they have to prevent breeding (for instance if an animal is too old to risk her giving birth safely) by giving contraceptive treatment.

Keepers, vet staff and outside specialists work together on a zebra.

Conservation starts at home; Paignton Zoo breeds British endangered species and re-introduces them to the wild. If populations are dying off in the wild it is important to find out if infectious disease is the cause. It is also important to make sure that the animals the Zoo breeds don't introduce new diseases to the wild populations. All animals undergo rigorous health screening according to IUCN guidelines before they are released.

As with all jobs there is a large amount of paperwork involved and keeping accurate records takes up a lot of time. However, staff can learn a lot and improve techniques by analysing the way things have been done and how animals responded to different anaesthetics and treatments. So, sitting down and reviewing techniques is important. Staff also have to report drug usage, write risk assessments and COSHH reports and all the other things involved in running a veterinary business.

A tiny dormouse is anaesthetised inside a face mask during health checks.

It's a hugely varied job and an incredible environment in which to work. The work is satisfying, frustrating, pressured and amazing.